This edition published 1995 by Geddes & Grosset Ltd,
David Dale House, New Lanark, Scotland

Illustrated by Lyndsay Duff in the style of Charles Robinson

ISBN 1 85534 531 5

Printed in Slovenia

Hey! Diddle, Diddle

Mother Goose Rhymes

Hey!
Diddle,
Diddle

HEY! DIDDLE, DIDDLE

HEY! diddle, diddle,

The cat and the fiddle,

The cow jumped over the moon;

The little dog laughed

To see such craft,

And the dish ran away with the
spoon.

TWO LITTLE BIRDS

There were two blackbirds

Sat upon a hill,

The one named Jack,

The other named Jill.

Fly away, Jack!

Fly away, Jill!

Come again, Jack!

Come again, Jill!

THE LITTLE COCK SPARROW

A LITTLE Cock Sparrow sat on a green tree,

And he chirruped, he chirruped, so merry was he;

A little Cock Sparrow sat on a green tree,

And he chirruped, he chirruped, so merry was he.

A naughty boy came with his wee bow and arrow,
Determined to shoot this little Cock Sparrow;
A naughty boy came with his wee bow and arrow,
Determined to shoot this little Cock Sparrow.

"This little Cock Sparrow shall make me a stew,
And his giblets shall make me a little pie too."
"Oh, no!" said the sparrow, "I won't make a stew."
So he flapped his wings and away he flew!

DAME TROT

Dame Trot and her
cat
Sat down for to
chat;
The Dame sat on
this side,
And Puss sat on that.

" Puss," says the Dame,
" Can you catch a rat
Or a mouse in the dark?"
" Purr," says the cat.

IF

F you are to be a gentleman, as I suppose
you be,

You 'll neither laugh nor smile for
a tickling of the knee.

HOW DO YOU DO?

How do you do, neighbour?
Neighbour, how do you do?
Very well, I thank you.
How does Cousin Sue do?
She is very well,
And sends her love to you,
And so does Cousin Bell.
Ah! how, pray, does she
do?

THERE WAS A LITTLE BOY

There was a little boy and
   a little girl,
  Lived in an alley;
Says the little boy to the
   little girl,
  " Shall I, oh, shall I?"

Says the little girl to the
   little boy,
  " What shall we do?"
     Says the little boy to the little girl,
      " I will kiss you."

THE MAN IN THE WILDERNESS

The man in the wilderness
   asked me,
How many strawberries grew
   in the sea?
I answered him, as I thought
   good,
As many as red herrings
   grew in the wood.

THOMAS A' TATTAMUS

THOMAS A' TATTAMUS took two T's

To tie two tups to two tall trees,

To frighten the terrible Thomas A' Tattamus!

Tell me how many T's there are in all that.

LITTLE GIRL, LITTLE GIRL

Little girl, little girl, where have you been?

Gathering roses to give to the Queen.

Little girl, little girl, what gave she you?

She gave me a diamond as big as my shoe.

LENGTHENING DAYS

As the days grow longer

The storms grow stronger

A MEDLEY

O N Christmas Eve I turned the spit,
I burnt my fingers, I feel it yet;
The cock sparrow flew over the table,
The pot began to play with the ladle;
The ladle stood up like a naked man,
And vowed he'd fight the frying-pan;
The frying-pan behind the door
Said he never saw the like before;
And the kitchen clock I was going to wind
Said he never saw the like behind.

THE WISE MEN OF GOTHAM

Three wise men of Gotham
They went to sea in a bowl;
And if the bowl had been stronger,
My song had been longer.

WEE WILLIE WINKIE

WEE WILLIE WINKIE runs through the town,

Up stairs and down stairs, in his night-gown,

Rapping at the window, crying through the lock:

"Are the children in their beds, for it's past eight o'clock."

BAA, BAA, BLACK SHEEP

Baa, baa, black sheep, have you any wool?

Yes, marry, have I, three bags full:

One for my master, one for my dame,

But none for the little boy who cries in the lane.

THE PIPER'S COW

There was a piper had a cow,
 And he had nought to give her;
He pulled out his pipe, and played
  her a tune,
 And bade the cow consider.

The cow considered very well,
 And gave the piper a penny,
And bade him play the other tune—
 " Corn rigs are bonny."

SHAVE A PIG

Barber, barber, shave a pig,

How many hairs will make a
 wig?

" Four and twenty, that 's
 enough,"

Give the barber a pinch of
 snuff.

EARLY RISING

HE that would thrive,

Must rise at five;

He that hath thriven,

May lie till seven;

And he that by the plough
would thrive,

Himself must either hold or drive.

THE TAILORS AND THE SNAIL

Four and twenty tailors went to kill a snail,

The best man amongst them durst not touch her tail;

She put out her horns like a little Kyloe cow,

Run, tailors, run, or she'll kill you all e'en now.

DOCTOR FAUSTUS

DOCTOR FAUSTUS was a good
man,
    He whipped his scholars now
    and then;
    When he whipped them he
    made them dance
Out of Scotland into France,
Out of France into Spain,
And then he whipped them back again.

POLLY, PUT
THE KETTLE ON

Polly, put the kettle on,
Polly, put the kettle on,
Polly, put the kettle on,
    And we'll have tea.
Sukey, take it off again,
Sukey, take it off again,
Sukey, take it off again,
    They're all gone away.

THE BLACKSMITH

ROBERT BARNES, fellow fine,
  Can you shoe this horse of mine?"
" Yes, good sir, that I can,
  As well as any other man;
  Here's a nail, and there's a prod,
  And now, good sir, your horse is shod."

THE FOUNT OF LEARNING

Here's A, B, and C, D, E, F, and G,
H, I, J, K, L, M, N, O, P, Q,
R, S, T, and U,
W, X, Y, and Z.
And here's the child's dad
Who is sagacious and discerning,
And knows this is the fount of all learning.

OF ARITHMETIC

MULTIPLICATION is vexation,
    Division is as bad;
The Rule of Three doth puzzle me,
    And Practice drives me mad.

OVER THE WATER
TO CHARLEY

Over the water, and over the lea,
And over the water to Charley.
Charley loves good ale and wine,
And Charley loves good brandy;
And Charley loves a pretty girl,
As sweet as sugar-candy.

Over the water, and over the sea,
And over the water to Charley,
I'll have none of your nasty beef,
Nor I'll have none of your barley;
But I'll have some of your very best flour,
To make a white cake for my Charley.

There were three jolly Welshmen,
　　As I have heard say,
And they went a-hunting
　　Upon St. David's day.

All the day they hunted,
　　And nothing could they find;

But a ship a-sailing,
    A-sailing with the wind.

One said it was a ship,
    The other he said "Nay";
The third he said it was a house,
    With the chimney blown away.

And all the night they hunted,
    And nothing could they find,
But the moon a-gliding,
    A-gliding with the wind.

One said it was the moon,
    The other he said "Nay";
The third he said it was a cheese,
    With half o' it cut away.

THE DAYS OF THE MONTH

THIRTY days hath September,
April, June, and November;
February has twenty-eight
alone,
All the rest have thirty-one,
Except in leap-year, when's the time
That February has twenty-nine.

A VARIED SONG

I 'll sing you a song,

The days are long,

The woodcock and the sparrow;

The little dog he has burned his
tail,

And he must be hanged to-morrow.

A diller, a dollar,
A ten o'clock scholar;
What makes you come so soon?
You used to come at ten o'clock,
But now you come at noon.

A PIE SAT ON A PEAR-TREE

A PIE sat on a pear-tree,
  A pie sat on a pear-tree,
  A pie sat on a pear-tree,
  Heigh O, heigh O, heigh O!
Once so merrily hopped she,
    Twice so merrily hopped she,
    Thrice so merrily hopped she,
Heigh O, heigh O, heigh O!

THE GIRL IN THE LANE

The girl in the lane, that couldn't speak plain,

Cried gobble, gobble, gobble;

The man on the hill, that couldn't stand still,

Went hobble, hobble, hobble.

THREE MEN IN A TUB

Rub-a-dub-dub,

Three men in a tub;

And who do you think they be?

The butcher, the baker,

The candlestick-maker;

Turn 'em out, knaves all three!

LITTLE MISS MUFFET

LITTLE Miss Muffet,
  She sat on a tuffet,
Eating of curds and whey;
  There came a big spider,
  And sat down beside her,
And frightened Miss Muffet away.

THE BOY AND
THE OWL

There was a little boy
  went into a field,
  And lay down on
  some hay;

An owl came out and
  flew about,
  And the little boy ran
  away.

A was an apple pie

B bit it,

C cut it,

D dealt it,

E eat it,

F fought for it,

G got it,

H had it,

J joined it,

K kept it,

L longed for it,

M mourned for it,